6 Full-Length PARCC Grade 5 Math Practice Tests

Extra Test Prep to Help Ace the PARCC Grade 5 Math Test

By

Michael Smith & Reza Nazari

6 Full-Length PARCC Grade 5 Math Practice Tests

Published in the United State of America By

The Math Notion

Web: WWW.MathNotion.Com

Email: info@Mathnotion.com

About the Author

Michael Smith has been a math instructor for over a decade now. He holds a master's degree in Management. Since 2006, Michael has devoted his time to both teaching and developing exceptional math learning materials. As a Math instructor and test prep expert, Michael has worked with thousands of students. He has used the feedback of his students to develop a unique study program that can be used by students to drastically improve their math score fast and effectively.

– SAT Math Practice Book

– ACT Math Practice Book

– GRE Math Practice Book

– Common Core Math Practice Book

–many Math Education Workbooks, Exercise Books and Study Guides

As an experienced Math teacher, Mr. Smith employs a variety of formats to help students achieve their goals: He tutors online and in person, he teaches students in large groups, and he provides training materials and textbooks through his website and through Amazon.

You can contact Michael via email at:

info@Mathnotion.com

Prepare for the PARCC Grade 5 Math test with a perfect practice book!

The surest way to practice your PARCC Math test-taking skills is with simulated exams. This comprehensive practice book with 6 full length and realistic PARCC Math practice tests help you measure your exam readiness, find your weak areas, and succeed on the PARCC Math test. The detailed answers and explanations for each PARCC Math question help you master every aspect of the PARCC Math.

6 Full-length PARCC Grade 5 Math Practice Tests is a prestigious resource to help you succeed on the PARCC Math test. This perfect practice book features:

- Content 100% aligned with the PARCC test
- Six full-length PARCC Math practice tests similar to the actual test in length, format, question types, and degree of difficulty
- Detailed answers and explanations for the PARCC Math practice questions
- Written by PARCC Math top instructors and experts

After completing this hands-on exercise book, you will gain confidence, strong foundation, and adequate practice to succeed on the PARCC Math test.

WWW.MathNotion.COM

… So Much More Online!

✓ FREE Math Lessons

✓ More Math Learning Books!

✓ Mathematics Worksheets

✓ Online Math Tutors

For a PDF Version of This Book

Please Visit WWW.MathNotion.com

Contents

PARCC Math Practice Tests

Time to Test

Time to refine your skill with a practice examination

Take a REAL PARCC Mathematics test to simulate the test day experience. After you've finished, score your test using the answer key.

Before You Start

- You'll need a pencil and scratch papers to take the test.

- For this practice test, don't time yourself. Spend time as much as you need.

- It's okay to guess. You won't lose any points if you're wrong.

- After you've finished the test, review the answer key to see where you went wrong.

Calculators are not permitted for Grade 5 PARCC Tests

Good Luck!

PARCC GRADE 5 MAHEMATICS REFRENCE MATERIALS

Perimeter

Square	$P = 4S$
Rectangle	$P = 2L + 2W$

Area

Square	$A = S \times S$
Rectangle	$A = l \times w$ or $A = bh$

Volume

Square	$A = S \times S \times S$
Rectangle	$A = l \times w \times h$ or $A = Bh$

LENGTH

Customary	Metric
1 mile (mi) = 1,760 yards (yd)	1 kilometer (km) = 1,000 meters (m)
1 yard (yd) = 3 feet (ft)	1 meter (m) = 100 centimeters (cm)
1 foot (ft) = 12 inches (in.)	1 centimeter (cm) = 10 millimeters (mm)

VOLUME AND CAPACITY

Customary	Metric
1 gallon (gal) = 4 quarts (qt)	1 liter (L) = 1,000 milliliters (mL)
1 quart (qt) = 2 pints (pt.)	
1 pint (pt.) = 2 cups (c)	
1 cup (c) = 8 fluid ounces (Fl oz)	

WEIGHT AND MASS

Customary	Metric
1 ton (T) = 2,000 pounds (lb.)	1 kilogram (kg) = 1,000 grams (g)
1 pound (lb.) = 16 ounces (oz)	1 gram (g) = 1,000 milligrams (mg)

Partnership for Assessment of Readiness for College and Careers (PARCC)

PARCC Practice Test 1

GRADE 5

Mathematics

Administered *Month Year*

Unit 1

Calculators are NOT permitted for unit 1 of the test.

Read each question. Then mark your answers in your answer sheet.

If you have time, review your answers and only answer questions you did not answer in the unit.

Time for Unit 1: 60 Minutes

1) The drivers at G & G trucking must report the mileage on their trucks each week. The mileage reading of Ed's vehicle was 21,890 at the beginning of one week, and 22,010 at the end of the same week. What was the total number of miles driven by Ed that week?

A. 420miles

B. 22 M miles

C. 120 miles

D. 1,420 miles

2) Camille uses a 15% off coupon when buying a sweater that costs $40. How much does she pay?

A. $34

B. $68

C. $104

D. $54

3) The area of a rectangle is D square feet and its length is 19 feet. Which equation represents W, the width of the rectangle in feet?

A. $W = \dfrac{D}{19}$

B. $W = \dfrac{19}{D}$

C. $W = 19D$

D. $W = 19 + D$

4) A baker uses 8 eggs to bake a cake. How many cakes will he be able to bake with 720 eggs?

    A. 75

    B. 90

    C. 96

    D. 60

5) Which list shows the fractions in order from least to greatest?

$$\frac{7}{10}, \frac{8}{9}, \frac{3}{5}, \frac{2}{16}, \frac{1}{2}$$

    A. $\frac{8}{9}, \frac{7}{10}, \frac{1}{2}, \frac{2}{16}, \frac{3}{5}$

    B. $\frac{3}{5}, \frac{2}{16}, \frac{8}{9}, \frac{7}{10}, \frac{1}{2}$

    C. $\frac{1}{2}, \frac{8}{9}, \frac{7}{10}, \frac{2}{16}, \frac{3}{5}$

    D. $\frac{2}{16}, \frac{1}{2}, \frac{3}{5}, \frac{7}{10}, \frac{8}{9}$

6) Which statement about 3 multiplied by $\frac{5}{4}$ is true?

    A. The product is between 4 and 5

    B. The product is between 3 and 4

    C. The product is more than $\frac{19}{4}$

    D. The product is between $\frac{11}{2}$ and 6

7) A shirt costing $160 is discounted 24%. Which of the following expressions can be used to find the selling price of the shirt?

    A. (160) (0.87)

    B. (160) – 160 (0.70)

    C. (160) (0.87) – (160) (0.24)

    D. (160) (0.76)

8) Which of the following angles is acute?

    A. 140 Degrees

    B. 125 Degrees

    C. 110 Degrees

    D. 80 Degrees

9) If A = 30, then which of the following equations are correct?

    A. $A + 40 = 70$

    B. $A \div 40 = 70$

    C. $40 \times A = 70$

    D. $A - 40 = 70$

10) The perimeter of the trapezoid below is 85. What is its area?

    Write your answer in the box below.

STOP
This is the end of Unit 1

Unit 2

Calculators are NOT permitted for unit 2 of the test.

Read each question. Then mark your answers in your answer sheet.

If you have time, review your answers and only answer questions you did not

answer in the unit.

Time for Unit 2: 60 Minutes

11) The area of a circle is 9π. What is the circumference of the circle?

    A. 18π

    B. 6π

    C. 9π

    D. 81π

12) The distance between cities A and B is approximately 1,406 miles. If Alice drive an average of 38 miles per hour, how many hours will it take Alice to drive from city A to city B?

    A. Approximately 49 Hours

    B. Approximately 37 Hours

    C. Approximately 35 Hours

    D. Approximately 40 Hours

13) 5 yards 9 feet and 13 inches equals to how many inches?

    A. 301

    B. 310

    C. 312

    D. 403

14) Which expression has a value of -13?

    A. $7 - (-5) + (-25)$

    B. $3 + (-3) \times (-9)$

    C. $-6 \times (-6) + (-4) \times (-9)$

    D. $(-7) \times (-4) + 5$

15) Solve.

$$\frac{7}{8} \times \frac{4}{7} =$$

A. $\frac{1}{2}$

B. $\frac{5}{8}$

C. $\frac{14}{40}$

D. $\frac{3}{7}$

16) The length of a rectangle is $\frac{7}{10}$ of inches and the width of the rectangle is $\frac{5}{14}$ of inches. What is the area of that rectangle?

Write your answer in the box below.

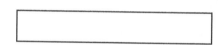

17) ABC Corporation earned only $420,000 during the previous year, seven–thirds only of the management's predicted income. How much earning did the management predict?

A. $45,000

B. $90,000

C. $180,000

D. $1,800,000

18) How many square feet of tile is needed for 11 feet to 11 feet room?

 A. 221 Square Feet

 B. 112 Square Feet

 C. 212 Square Feet

 D. 121 Square Feet

19) Solve. $\frac{5}{7} + \frac{1}{2} - \frac{3}{14} =$

 A. $\frac{5}{14}$

 B. $\frac{1}{7}$

 C. 1

 D. 14

20) Of the 2,800 videos available for rent at a certain video store, 896 are comedies.

 What percent of the videos are comedies?

 A. 0.30 %

 B. 1.30%

 C. 130%

 D. 32%

STOP

This is the end of Unit 2

Unit 3

Calculators are NOT permitted for unit 3 of the test.

Read each question. Then mark your answers in your answer sheet.

If you have time, review your answers and only answer questions you did not answer in the unit.

Time for Unit 3: 60 Minutes

21) In a bag, there are 84 cards. Of these cards, 12 cards are white. What fraction of the cards are white?

   A. $\frac{1}{7}$

   B. $\frac{4}{7}$

   C. $\frac{4}{21}$

   D. $\frac{7}{15}$

22) A rope weighs 280 grams per meter of length. What is the weight in kilograms of 10.5 meters of this rope? (1 kilograms = 1000 grams)

   A. 0.0294

   B. 0.294

   C. 2.94

   D. 2,940

23) Lily and Ella are in a pancake–eating contest. Lily can eat four pancakes per minute, while Ella can eat $3\frac{1}{4}$ pancakes per minute. How many total pancakes can they eat in 8 minutes?

   A. 8 Pancakes

   B. 38 Pancakes

   C. 28 Pancakes

   D. 58 Pancakes

24) How many $\frac{1}{7}$ cup servings are in a package of cheese that contains $2\frac{5}{7}$ cups altogether?

Write your answer in the box below.

25) With what number must 4.861248 be multiplied in order to obtain the number 486,124.8?

A. 10

B. 100

C. 1,000,000

D. 100,000

26) How many 3×3 squares can fit inside a rectangle with a height of 90 and width of 35?

A. 350

B. 305

C. 150

D. 150

27) What is the volume of this box?

A. 35 cm³

B. 77 cm³

C. 584 cm³

D. 385 cm³

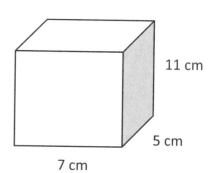

11 cm

5 cm

7 cm

28) William keeps track of the length of each fish that he catches. Following are the lengths in inches of the fish that he caught one day:

$$23, 27, 10, 29, 15, 21, 31$$

What is the median fish length that William caught that day?

   A. 31 Inches

   B. 29 Inches

   C. 27 Inches

   D. 23 Inches

29) $7 + [10 \times 9] \div 15 =?$

Write your answer in the box below.

```

```

30) 15 is What percent of 50?

   A. 15 %

   B. 20 %

   C. 30 %

   D. 45 %

"This is the end of Practice Test 1"

Partnership for Assessment of Readiness for College and Careers (PARCC)

PARCC Practice Test 2

GRADE 5

Mathematics

Administered *Month Year*

Unit 1

Calculators are NOT permitted for unit 1 of the test.

Read each question. Then mark your answers in your answer sheet.

If you have time, review your answers and only answer questions you did not answer in the unit.

Time for Unit 1: 60 Minutes

1) Jack added 32 to the product of 14 and 15. What is this sum?

  A. 442

  B. 424

  C. 242

  D. 2,424

2) Joe makes $6.25 per hour at his work. If he works 5 hours, how much money will he earn?

  A. $35.75

  B. $30.75

  C. $35.25

  D. $31.25

3) What is the value of $5 - 3\frac{2}{5}$?

  A. $\frac{13}{5}$

  B. $1\frac{3}{5}$

  C. $-2\frac{1}{5}$

  D. $\frac{24}{5}$

4) The bride and groom invited 240 guests for their wedding. 180 guests arrived.

What percent of the guest list was not present?

A. 14%

B. 18%

C. 24%

D. 25%

5) Frank wants to compare these two measurements.

52.756 kg ☐ 52,756 g

Which symbol should he use?

A. <

B. >

C. ≠

D. =

6) Aria was hired to teach four identical 5th grade math courses, which entailed being present in the classroom 24 hours altogether. At $30 per class hour, how much did Aria earn for teaching one course?

A. $70

B. $180

C. $580

D. $1,240

7) In a classroom of 80 students, 48 are male. What percentage of the class is female?

A. 60%

B. 20%

C. 40%

D. 85%

8) In a party, 6 soft drinks are required for every 18 guests. If there are 210 guests, how many soft drinks are required?

A. 58

B. 90

C. 70

D. 1,200

9) You are asked to chart the temperature during an 8–hour period to give the average. These are your results:

7 am: 5 degrees

8 am: 7 degrees

9 am: 15 degrees

10 am: 15 degrees

11 am: 23 degrees

12 pm: 26 degrees

1 pm: 33 degrees

2 pm: 36 degrees

What is the average temperature?

A. 20

B. 25

C. 18

D. 15

10) While at work, Emma checks her email once every 50 minutes. In 15 hours, how many times does she check her email?

A. 15 Times

B. 18 Times

C. 10 Times

D. 13 Times

STOP

This is the end of Unit 1

Unit 2

Calculators are NOT permitted for unit 2 of the test.

Read each question. Then mark your answers in your answer sheet.

If you have time, review your answers and only answer questions you did not answer in the unit.

Time for Unit 2: 60 Minutes

11) Peter traveled 160 miles in 8 hours and Jason traveled 400 miles in 8 hours. What is the ratio of the average speed of Peter to average speed of Jason?

A. 2: 5

B. 5: 2

C. 7: 3

D. 3: 5

12) A woman owns a dog walking business. If 5 workers can walk 10 dogs, how many dogs can 9 workers walk?

A. 9

B. 18

C. 36

D. 42

13) Which list shows the fractions listed in order from least to greatest?

$$\frac{1}{3}, \frac{1}{16}, \frac{1}{5}, \frac{1}{8}$$

A. $\frac{1}{8}, \frac{1}{3}, \frac{1}{16}, \frac{1}{5}$

B. $\frac{1}{5}, \frac{1}{16}, \frac{1}{3}, \frac{1}{8}$

C. $\frac{1}{3}, \frac{1}{5}, \frac{1}{8}, \frac{1}{16}$

D. $\frac{1}{16}, \frac{1}{8}, \frac{1}{5}, \frac{1}{3}$

14) What are the coordinates of the intersection of $x-axis$ and the $y-axis$ on a coordinate plane?

A. $(0, -5)$

B. $(5, 0)$

C. $(0, 0)$

D. $(0, 5)$

15) In a triangle ABC the measure of angle ACB is $48°$ and the measure of angle CAB is $72°$. What is the measure of angle ABC?

A. 50

B. 60

C. 40

D. 38

16) David's motorcycle stalled at the beach and he called the towing company. They charged him $ 3.95 per mile for the first 25 miles and then $4.15 per mile for each mile over 25. David was 29 miles from the motorcycle repair shop. How much was David's towing bill?

A. $145.55

B. $113.25

C. $115.35

D. $185.25

17) A car uses 25 gallons of gas to travel 1,000 miles. How many miles per gallon does the car get?

   A. 32 miles per gallon

   B. 30 miles per gallon

   C. 40 miles per gallon

   D. 25 miles per gallon

18) six out of 54 students had to go to summer school. What is the ratio of students who did not have to go to summer school expressed, in its lowest terms?

Write your answer in the box below.

```
┌─────────────────────────┐
│                         │
└─────────────────────────┘
```

19) A steak dinner at a restaurant costs $4.75. If a man buys a steak dinner for himself and 3 friends, what will the total cost be?

   A. $21.25

   B. $24.25

   C. $19.50

   D. $19

20) If 8 garbage trucks can collect the trash of 64 homes in a day. How many trucks are needed to collect in 160 houses?

   A. 28

   B. 52

   C. 15

   D. 20

STOP
This is the end of Unit 2

Unit 3

Calculators are NOT permitted for unit 3 of the test.

Read each question. Then mark your answers in your answer sheet.

If you have time, review your answers and only answer questions you did not

answer in the unit.

Time for Unit 3: 60 Minutes

21) In a classroom of 40 students, 18 are male. About what percentage of the class is female?

   A. 50%

   B. 52%

   C. 55%

   D. 45%

22) A florist has 833 flowers. How many full bouquets of 17 flowers can he make?

   A. 52

   B. 40

   C. 43

   D. 49

23) What is 5,157.59325 rounded to the nearest tenth?

   A. 5,157.593

   B. 5,157.6

   C. 5,157

   D. 5,157.59

24) If a rectangular swimming pool has a perimeter of 110 feet and it is 21 feet wide, what is its area?

   A. 654 square feet

   B. 514 square feet

   C. 417 square feet

   D. 714 square feet

25) What is the volume of the following rectangle prism?

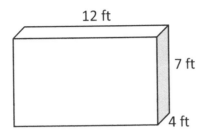

Write your answer in the box below.

26) A barista averages making 8 cups of coffee per hour. At this rate, how many

hours will it take until she's made 600 cups of coffee?

A. 70

B. 75

C. 65

D. 50

27) Ava needs $\frac{1}{5}$ of an ounce of salt to make 1 cup of dip for fries. How many cups

of dip will she be able to make if she has 56 ounces of salt?

A. 86

B. 28

C. 260

D. 280

28) A circle has a diameter of 12 inches. What is its approximate circumference?

($\pi = 3.14$)

A. 27.68 inches

B. 37.68 inches

C. 18.68 inches

D. 36.68 inches

29) How long is the line segment shown on the number line below?

Write your answer in the box below.

30) If $x = -3$, which equation is true?

A. $x(2x - 2) = 18$

B. $3(6 - 3x) = 45$

C. $4(3x + 7) = 16$

D. $6x - 8 = -15$

"This is the end of Practice Test 2"

Partnership for Assessment of Readiness for College and Careers (PARCC)

PARCC Practice Test 3

GRADE 5

Mathematics

Administered Month Year

Unit 1

Calculators are NOT permitted for unit 1 of the test.

Read each question. Then mark your answers in your answer sheet.

If you have time, review your answers and only answer questions you did not

answer in the unit.

Time for Unit 1: 60 Minutes

1) The drivers at G & G trucking must report the mileage on their trucks each week. The mileage reading of Ed's vehicle was 43,907 at the beginning of one week, and 44,053 at the end of the same week. What was the total number of miles driven by Ed that week?

   A. 46 MILES

   B. 145 MILES

   C. 146 MILES

   D. 1,046 MILES

2) Camille uses a 40% off coupon when buying a sweater that costs $30. How much does she pay?

   A. $18

   B. $25

   C. $40.50

   D. $43

3) The area of a rectangle is D square feet and its length is 7 feet. Which equation represents W, the width of the rectangle in feet?

   A. $W = \frac{D}{7}$

   B. $W = \frac{7}{D}$

   C. $W = 7D$

   D. $W = 7 + D$

4) A baker uses 3 eggs to bake a cake. How many cakes will he be able to bake with 210 eggs?

    A. 65

    B. 70

    C. 56

    D. 45

5) Which list shows the fractions in order from least to greatest?

$$\frac{3}{4}, \frac{6}{7}, \frac{2}{10}, \frac{1}{2}, \frac{6}{14}$$

    A. $\frac{3}{4}, \frac{6}{7}, \frac{2}{10}, \frac{1}{2}, \frac{6}{14}$

    B. $\frac{6}{14}, \frac{1}{2}, \frac{3}{4}, \frac{6}{7}, \frac{2}{10}$

    C. $\frac{2}{10}, \frac{3}{4}, \frac{6}{7}, \frac{1}{2}, \frac{6}{14}$

    D. $\frac{2}{10}, \frac{6}{14}, \frac{1}{2}, \frac{3}{4}, \frac{6}{7}$

6) Which statement about 5 multiplied by $\frac{4}{3}$ is true?

    A. The product is between 3 and 4

    B. The product is between 6 and 7

    C. The product is more than $\frac{11}{3}$

    D. The product is between $\frac{14}{3}$ and 5

7) A shirt costing $150 is discounted 10%. Which of the following expressions can be used to find the selling price of the shirt?

    A. (150) (0.70)

    B. (150) – 150 (0.30)

    C. (150) (0.15) – (150) (0.15)

    D. (150) (0.9)

8) Which of the following angles is obtuse?

    A. 30 Degrees

    B. 45 Degrees

    C. 80 Degrees

    D. 120 Degrees

9) If A = 30, then which of the following equations are correct?

    A. $A + 30 = 60$

    B. $A \div 30 = 60$

    C. $30 \times A = 60$

    D. $A - 30 = 60$

10) The perimeter of the trapezoid below is 50. What is its area?

    Write your answer in the box below.

16

10

12

STOP
This is the end of Unit 1

Unit 2

Calculators are NOT permitted for unit 2 of the test.

Read each question. Then mark your answers in your answer sheet.

If you have time, review your answers and only answer questions you did not answer in the unit.

Time for Unit 2: 60 Minutes

11) The area of a circle is 36π. What is the circumference of the circle?

    A. 8 π

    B. 12 π

    C. 32 π

    D. 64 π

12) The distance between cities A and B is approximately 1,960 miles. If Alice drive an average of 56 miles per hour, how many hours will it take Alice to drive from city A to city B?

    A. Approximately 41 Hours

    B. Approximately 35 Hours

    C. Approximately 29 Hours

    D. Approximately 27 Hours

13) 10 yards 3 feet and 4 inches equals to how many inches?

    A. 96

    B. 432

    C. 400

    D. 578

14) Which expression has a value of − 7?

    A. $7 - (-3) + (-17)$

    B. $1 + (-3) \times (-2)$

    C. $-6 \times (-6) + (-2) \times (-12)$

    D. $(-2) \times (-7) + 4$

15) Solve.

$$\frac{6}{8} \times \frac{4}{6} =$$

A. $\frac{1}{2}$

B. $\frac{10}{40}$

C. $\frac{20}{60}$

D. $\frac{1}{4}$

16) The length of a rectangle is $\frac{5}{6}$ of inches and the width of the rectangle is $\frac{2}{15}$ of inches. What is the area of that rectangle?

Write your answer in the box below.

17) ABC Corporation earned only $300,000 during the previous year, three–second only of the management's predicted income. How much earning did the management predict?

A. $30,000

B. $20,000

C. $200,000

D. $240,000

18) How many square feet of tile is needed for 16 feet to 16 feet room?

A. 85 Square Feet

B. 120 Square Feet

C. 216 Square Feet

D. 256 Square Feet

19) Solve. $\frac{1}{2} + \frac{4}{7} - \frac{1}{14} =$

A. $\frac{9}{10}$

B. $\frac{2}{10}$

C. 1

D. 14

20) Of the 3,600 videos available for rent at a certain video store, 900 are comedies.

What percent of the videos are comedies?

A. 18 ½ %

B. 20%

C. 22%

D. 25%

STOP

This is the end of Unit 2

Unit 3

Calculators are NOT permitted for unit 3 of the test.

Read each question. Then mark your answers in your answer sheet.

If you have time, review your answers and only answer questions you did not answer in the unit.

Time for Unit 3: 60 Minutes

21) In a bag, there are 40 cards. Of these cards, 8 cards are white. What fraction of the cards are white?

A. $\frac{1}{5}$

B. $\frac{4}{10}$

C. $\frac{32}{40}$

D. $\frac{2}{20}$

22) A rope weighs 500 grams per meter of length. What is the weight in kilograms of 12.2 meters of this rope? (1 kilograms = 1000 grams)

A. 0.061

B. 0.61

C. 6.1

D. 6,100

23) Lily and Ella are in a pancake–eating contest. Lily can eat three pancakes per minute, while Ella can eat 2 ½ pancakes per minute. How many total pancakes can they eat in 5 minutes?

A. 9.5 Pancakes

B. 29.5 Pancakes

C. 22.5 Pancakes

D. 27.5 Pancakes

24) How many $\frac{1}{4}$ cup servings are in a package of cheese that contains $5\frac{1}{2}$ cups

altogether?

Write your answer in the box below.

25) With what number must 5.253691 be multiplied in order to obtain the number

52,536.91?

A. 100

B. 1,000

C. 10,000

D. 100,000

26) How many 3 × 3 squares can fit inside a rectangle with a height of 52 and width

of 18?

A. 104

B. 85

C. 60

D. 88

27) What is the volume of this box?

A. 124 cm³

B. 86 cm³

C. 280 cm³

D. 315 cm³

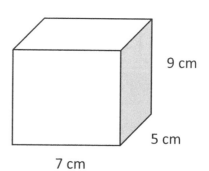

28) William keeps track of the length of each fish that he catches. Following are the lengths in inches of the fish that he caught one day: 15, 16, 9, 14, 9, 10, 18

What is the median fish length that William caught that day?

    A. 18 Inches

    B. 9 Inches

    C. 10 Inches

    D. 14 Inches

29) $6 + [6 \times 5] \div 2 = ?$

Write your answer in the box below.

30) 25 is What percent of 40?

    A. 20 %

    B. 62 %

    C. 62.5 %

    D. 150 %

"This is the end of Practice Test 3"

Partnership for Assessment of Readiness for College and Careers (PARCC)

Practice Test 4

GRADE 5

Mathematics

Administered Month Year

Unit 1

Calculators are NOT permitted for unit 1 of the test.

Read each question. Then mark your answers in your answer sheet.

If you have time, review your answers and only answer questions you did not answer in the unit.

Time for Unit 1: 60 Minutes

1) Jack added 16 to the product of 14 and 22. What is this sum?

   A. 86

   B. 336

   C. 324

   D. 7,602

2) Joe makes $4.75 per hour at his work. If he works 6 hours, how much money will he earn?

   A. $33.00

   B. $32.75

   C. $36.50

   D. $28.5

3) What is the value of $5 - 3\frac{2}{9}$?

   A. $\frac{23}{9}$

   B. $1\frac{7}{9}$

   C. $-\frac{1}{9}$

   D. $\frac{42}{9}$

4) The bride and groom invited 230 guests for their wedding. 190 guests arrived.

What percent of the guest list was not present?

A. 70%

B. 40%

C. 43.32%

D. 17.4%

5) Frank wants to compare these two measurements.

19.023 kg ☐ 19,023 g

Which symbol should he use?

A. <

B. >

C. ≠

D. =

6) Aria was hired to teach three identical 5th grade math courses, which entailed

being present in the classroom 24 hours altogether. At $20 per class hour, how

much did Aria earn for teaching one course?

A. $50

B. $160

C. $300

D. $1,400

7) In a classroom of 50 students, 25 are male. What percentage of the class is female?

A. 25%

B. 40%

C. 50%

D. 75%

8) In a party, 8 soft drinks are required for every 12 guests. If there are 156 guests, how many soft drinks are required?

A. 18

B. 36

C. 104

D. 171

9) You are asked to chart the temperature during an 8–hour period to give the average. These are your results:

7 am: 3 degrees   11 am: 31 degrees

8 am: 6 degrees   12 pm: 34 degrees

9 am: 23 degrees   1 pm: 34 degrees

10 am: 29 degrees   2 pm: 32 degrees

What is the average temperature?

A. 24

B. 28

C. 36

D. 46

10) While at work, Emma checks her email once every 90 minutes. In 12 hours, how many times does she check her email?

A. 9 Times

B. 8 Times

C. 6 Times

D. 7 Times

STOP

This is the end of Unit 1

Unit 2

Calculators are NOT permitted for unit 2 of the test.

Read each question. Then mark your answers in your answer sheet.

If you have time, review your answers and only answer questions you did not

answer in the unit.

Time for Unit 2: 60 Minutes

11) Peter traveled 160 miles in 4 hours and Jason traveled 240 miles in 8 hours. What is the ratio of the average speed of Peter to average speed of Jason?

A. 4: 3

B. 2: 3

C. 5: 7

D. 5: 6

12) A woman owns a dog walking business. If 3 workers can walk 9 dogs, how many dogs can 6 workers walk?

A. 12

B. 18

C. 16

D. 19

13) Which list shows the fractions listed in order from least to greatest?

$$\frac{1}{3}, \frac{1}{10}, \frac{1}{6}, \frac{1}{8}$$

A. $\frac{1}{8}, \frac{1}{3}, \frac{1}{10}, \frac{1}{6}$

B. $\frac{1}{6}, \frac{1}{10}, \frac{1}{3}, \frac{1}{8}$

C. $\frac{1}{3}, \frac{1}{6}, \frac{1}{8}, \frac{1}{10}$

D. $\frac{1}{10}, \frac{1}{8}, \frac{1}{6}, \frac{1}{3}$

14) What are the coordinates of the intersection of $x-axis$ and the $y-axis$ on a coordinate plane?

   A. (5, 5)

   B. (1, 1)

   C. (0, 0)

   D. (0, 1)

15) In a triangle ABC the measure of angle ACB is 35° and the measure of angle CAB is 65°. What is the measure of angle ABC?

   A. 100

   B. 80

   C. 55

   D. 25

16) David's motorcycle stalled at the beach and he called the towing company. They charged him $ 3.75 per mile for the first 20 miles and then $4.15 per mile for each mile over 20. David was 28 miles from the motorcycle repair shop. How much was David's towing bill?

   A. $105

   B. $113

   C. $108.20

   D. $116.20

17) A car uses 15 gallons of gas to travel 675 miles. How many miles per gallon does the car get?

    A. 26 miles per gallon

    B. 28 miles per gallon

    C. 45 miles per gallon

    D. 35 miles per gallon

18) Five out of 35 students had to go to summer school. What is the ratio of students who did not have to go to summer school expressed, in its lowest terms?

Write your answer in the box below.

19) A steak dinner at a restaurant costs $8.5. If a man buys a steak dinner for himself and 3 friends, what will the total cost be?

    A. $42.50

    B. $34.00

    C. $25.50

    D. $17.00

20) If 4 garbage trucks can collect the trash of 32 homes in a day. How many trucks are needed to collect in 80 houses?

    A. 8

    B. 9

    C. 5

    D. 10

STOP
This is the end of Unit 2

Unit 3

Calculators are NOT permitted for unit 3 of the test.

Read each question. Then mark your answers in your answer sheet.

If you have time, review your answers and only answer questions you did not answer in the unit.

Time for Unit 3: 60 Minutes

21) In a classroom of 66 students, 30 are male. About what percentage of the class is female?

   A. 53%

   B. 54%

   C. 55%

   D. 56%

22) A florist has 585 flowers. How many full bouquets of 13 flowers can he make?

   A. 40

   B. 41

   C. 43

   D. 45

23) What is 6,123.48245 rounded to the nearest tenth?

   A. 6,123.482

   B. 6,123.5

   C. 6,123

   D. 6,123.48

24) If a rectangular swimming pool has a perimeter of 124 feet and it is 24 feet wide, what is its area?

   A. 1,896 square feet

   B. 2,600 square feet

   C. 1,325 square feet

   D. 912 square feet

25) What is the volume of the following rectangle prism?

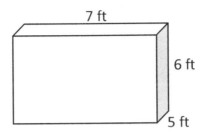

Write your answer in the box below.

26) A barista averages making 12 cups of coffee per hour. At this rate, how many hours will it take until she's made 1080 cups of coffee?

A. 75

B. 90

C. 85

D. 90

27) Ava needs 1/5 of an ounce of salt to make 1 cup of dip for fries. How many cups of dip will she be able to make if she has 60 ounces of salt?

A. 45

B. 55

C. 75

D. 300

28) A circle has a diameter of 4 inches. What is its approximate circumference? (π = 3.14)

    A. 6.23 inches

    B. 12.56 inches

    C. 32.65 inches

    D. 36.12 inches

29) How long is the line segment shown on the number line below?

Write your answer in the box below.

30) If $x = -2$, which equation is true?

    A. $x(2x - 4) = 50$

    B. $8(4 - x) = 48$

    C. $2(4x + 6) = 10$

    D. $6x - 2 = -23$

"This is the end of Practice Test 4"

Partnership for Assessment of Readiness for College and Careers (PARCC)

PARCC Practice Test 5

GRADE 5

Mathematics

Administered *Month Year*

Unit 1

Calculators are NOT permitted for unit 1 of the test.

Read each question. Then mark your answers in your answer sheet.

If you have time, review your answers and only answer questions you did not answer in the unit.

Time for Unit 1: 60 Minutes

1) The drivers at G & G trucking must report the mileage on their trucks each week. The mileage reading of Ed's vehicle was 54,815 at the beginning of one week, and 55,015 at the end of the same week. What was the total number of miles driven by Ed that week?

   A. 815 miles

   B. 20 M miles

   C. 200 miles

   D. 1,200 miles

2) Camille uses a 20% off coupon when buying a sweater that costs $50. How much does she pay?

   A. $40

   B. $80

   C. $100

   D. $32

3) The area of a rectangle is D square feet and its length is 10 feet. Which equation represents W, the width of the rectangle in feet?

   A. $W = \dfrac{D}{10}$

   B. $W = \dfrac{10}{D}$

   C. $W = 10D$

   D. $W = 10 + D$

4) A baker uses 6 eggs to bake a cake. How many cakes will he be able to bake with 300 eggs?

    A. 65

    B. 50

    C. 56

    D. 45

5) Which list shows the fractions in order from least to greatest?

$$\frac{2}{3}, \frac{5}{8}, \frac{3}{10}, \frac{1}{4}, \frac{5}{16}$$

    A. $\frac{2}{3}, \frac{5}{8}, \frac{3}{10}, \frac{1}{4}, \frac{5}{16}$

    B. $\frac{5}{16}, \frac{1}{4}, \frac{2}{3}, \frac{5}{8}, \frac{3}{10}$

    C. $\frac{3}{10}, \frac{2}{3}, \frac{5}{8}, \frac{1}{4}, \frac{5}{16}$

    D. $\frac{1}{4}, \frac{3}{10}, \frac{5}{16}, \frac{5}{8}, \frac{2}{3}$

6) Which statement about 2 multiplied by $\frac{7}{3}$ is true?

    A. The product is between 3 and 4

    B. The product is between 4 and 5

    C. The product is more than $\frac{17}{3}$

    D. The product is between $\frac{16}{3}$ and 6

7) A shirt costing $250 is discounted 30%. Which of the following expressions can be used to find the selling price of the shirt?

A. (250) (0.80)

B. (250) – 250 (0.70)

C. (250) (0.30) – (250) (0.30)

D. (250) (0.7)

8) Which of the following angles is acute?

A. 130 Degrees

B. 145 Degrees

C. 120 Degrees

D. 50 Degrees

9) If A = 40, then which of the following equations are correct?

A. $A + 50 = 90$

B. $A \div 50 = 90$

C. $50 \times A = 90$

D. $A - 50 = 90$

10) The perimeter of the trapezoid below is 100. What is its area?

Write your answer in the box below.

STOP
This is the end of Unit 1

Unit 2

Calculators are NOT permitted for unit 2 of the test.

Read each question. Then mark your answers in your answer sheet.

If you have time, review your answers and only answer questions you did not answer in the unit.

Time for Unit 2: 60 Minutes

11) The area of a circle is 16π. What is the circumference of the circle?

    A. $16\,\pi$

    B. $8\,\pi$

    C. $32\,\pi$

    D. $64\,\pi$

12) The distance between cities A and B is approximately 1,890 miles. If Alice drive an average of 42 miles per hour, how many hours will it take Alice to drive from city A to city B?

    A. Approximately 41 Hours

    B. Approximately 45 Hours

    C. Approximately 39 Hours

    D. Approximately 47 Hours

13) 6 yards 8 feet and 10 inches equals to how many inches?

    A. 216

    B. 422

    C. 322

    D. 521

14) Which expression has a value of -10?

    A. $8 - (-4) + (-22)$

    B. $2 + (-4) \times (-5)$

    C. $-5 \times (-5) + (-3) \times (-13)$

    D. $(-5) \times (-6) + 8$

15) Solve.

$$\frac{5}{9} \times \frac{3}{5} =$$

A. $\frac{1}{3}$

B. $\frac{15}{40}$

C. $\frac{20}{45}$

D. $\frac{1}{2}$

16) The length of a rectangle is $\frac{4}{9}$ of inches and the width of the rectangle is $\frac{3}{16}$ of inches. What is the area of that rectangle?

Write your answer in the box below.

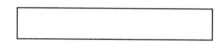

17) ABC Corporation earned only $600,000 during the previous year, five–thirds only of the management's predicted income. How much earning did the management predict?

A. $30,000

B. $60,000

C. $360,000

D. $1,000,000

18) How many square feet of tile is needed for 13 feet to 13 feet room?

    A. 26 Square Feet

    B. 144 Square Feet

    C. 216 Square Feet

    D. 169 Square Feet

19) Solve. $\frac{2}{3} + \frac{3}{5} - \frac{10}{15} =$

    A. $\frac{3}{10}$

    B. $\frac{2}{5}$

    C. $\frac{3}{5}$

    D. 15

20) Of the 4,200 videos available for rent at a certain video store, 840 are comedies.

    What percent of the videos are comedies?

    A. 0.20 %

    B. 1.20%

    C. 120%

    D. 20%

STOP

This is the end of Unit 2

Unit 3

Calculators are NOT permitted for unit 3 of the test.

Read each question. Then mark your answers in your answer sheet.

If you have time, review your answers and only answer questions you did not answer in the unit.

Time for Unit 3: 60 Minutes

21) In a bag, there are 50 cards. Of these cards, 10 cards are white. What fraction of the cards are white?

   A. $\frac{1}{5}$

   B. $\frac{4}{10}$

   C. $\frac{4}{5}$

   D. $\frac{1}{10}$

22) A rope weighs 650 grams per meter of length. What is the weight in kilograms of 11.8 meters of this rope? (1 kilograms = 1000 grams)

   A. 0.0767

   B. 0.767

   C. 7.67

   D. 7,670

23) Lily and Ella are in a pancake–eating contest. Lily can eat five pancakes per minute, while Ella can eat $4\frac{1}{3}$ pancakes per minute. How many total pancakes can they eat in 6 minutes?

   A. 6 Pancakes

   B. 30 Pancakes

   C. 26 Pancakes

   D. 56 Pancakes

24) How many $\frac{1}{3}$ cup servings are in a package of cheese that contains $4\frac{2}{3}$ cups altogether?

Write your answer in the box below.

25) With what number must 6.346367 be multiplied in order to obtain the number 634,636.7?

A. 100

B. 1,000

C. 10,000

D. 100,000

26) How many 4 × 4 squares can fit inside a rectangle with a height of 80 and width of 24?

A. 120

B. 104

C. 160

D. 320

27) What is the volume of this box?

A. 160 cm^3

B. 80 cm^3

C. 240 cm^3

D. 480 cm^3

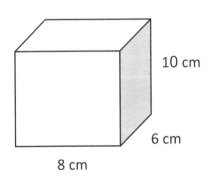

10 cm

6 cm

8 cm

28) William keeps track of the length of each fish that he catches. Following are the lengths in inches of the fish that he caught one day:

$$25, 26, 9, 24, 19, 20, 28$$

What is the median fish length that William caught that day?

A. 28 Inches

B. 19 Inches

C. 20 Inches

D. 24 Inches

29) $9 + [4 \times 8] \div 16 = ?$

Write your answer in the box below.

30) 35 is What percent of 80?

A. 40 %

B. 43 %

C. 43.75 %

D. 87.5 %

"This is the end of Practice Test 5"

Partnership for Assessment of Readiness for College and Careers (PARCC)

PARCC Practice Test 6

GRADE 5

Mathematics

Administered *Month Year*

Unit 1

Calculators are NOT permitted for unit 1 of the test.

Read each question. Then mark your answers in your answer sheet.

If you have time, review your answers and only answer questions you did not answer in the unit.

Time for Unit 1: 60 Minutes

1) Jack added 26 to the product of 24 and 32. What is this sum?

    A. 768

    B. 672

    C. 794

    D. 7,904

2) Joe makes $5.75 per hour at his work. If he works 7 hours, how much money

    will he earn?

    A. $33.25

    B. $33.75

    C. $36.25

    D. $40.25

3) What is the value of $6 - 4\frac{1}{7}$?

    A. $\frac{23}{7}$

    B. $1\frac{6}{7}$

    C. $-\frac{1}{7}$

    D. $\frac{42}{7}$

4) The bride and groom invited 350 guests for their wedding. 280 guests arrived. What percent of the guest list was not present?

A. 70%

B. 28%

C. 23.32%

D. 20%

5) Frank wants to compare these two measurements.

28.045 kg ☐ 28,045 g

Which symbol should he use?

A. <

B. >

C. ≠

D. =

6) Aria was hired to teach three identical 5ᵗʰ grade math courses, which entailed being present in the classroom 21 hours altogether. At $25 per class hour, how much did Aria earn for teaching one course?

A. $75

B. $175

C. $525

D. $1,575

7) In a classroom of 70 students, 42 are male. What percentage of the class is female?

A. 28%

B. 30%

C. 40%

D. 75%

8) In a party, 5 soft drinks are required for every 14 guests. If there are 280 guests, how many soft drinks are required?

A. 18

B. 70

C. 100

D. 1,400

9) You are asked to chart the temperature during an 8–hour period to give the average. These are your results:

7 am: 4 degrees   11 am: 24 degrees

8 am: 5 degrees   12 pm: 31 degrees

9 am: 10 degrees   1 pm: 35 degrees

10 am: 14 degrees   2 pm: 37 degrees

What is the average temperature?

A. 20

B. 24

C. 21

D. 19

10) While at work, Emma checks her email once every 80 minutes. In 16 hours, how many times does she check her email?

A. 9 Times

B. 12 Times

C. 8 Times

D. 5 Times

STOP

This is the end of Unit 1

Unit 2

Calculators are NOT permitted for unit 2 of the test.

Read each question. Then mark your answers in your answer sheet.

If you have time, review your answers and only answer questions you did not answer in the unit.

Time for Unit 2: 60 Minutes

11) Peter traveled 210 miles in 7 hours and Jason traveled 360 miles in 9 hours. What is the ratio of the average speed of Peter to average speed of Jason?

A. 3 : 4

B. 3 : 2

C. 7 : 9

D. 6 : 5

12) A woman owns a dog walking business. If 2 workers can walk 8 dogs, how many dogs can 7 workers walk?

A. 14

B. 28

C. 26

D. 32

13) Which list shows the fractions listed in order from least to greatest?

$$\frac{1}{4}, \frac{1}{11}, \frac{1}{7}, \frac{1}{9}$$

A. $\frac{1}{9}, \frac{1}{4}, \frac{1}{11}, \frac{1}{7}$

B. $\frac{1}{7}, \frac{1}{11}, \frac{1}{4}, \frac{1}{9}$

C. $\frac{1}{4}, \frac{1}{7}, \frac{1}{9}, \frac{1}{11}$

D. $\frac{1}{11}, \frac{1}{9}, \frac{1}{7}, \frac{1}{4}$

14) What are the coordinates of the intersection of $x-axis$ and the $y-axis$ on a coordinate plane?

A. $(0, -1)$

B. $(1, 0)$

C. $(0, 0)$

D. $(0, 1)$

15) In a triangle ABC the measure of angle ACB is $45°$ and the measure of angle CAB is $60°$. What is the measure of angle ABC?

A. 80

B. 75

C. 45

D. 30

16) David's motorcycle stalled at the beach and he called the towing company. They charged him $ 4.25 per mile for the first 30 miles and then $4.75 per mile for each mile over 30. David was 39 miles from the motorcycle repair shop. How much was David's towing bill?

A. $127.5

B. $117.5

C. $170.25

D. $165.25

17) A car uses 18 gallons of gas to travel 990 miles. How many miles per gallon does the car get?

A. 36 miles per gallon

B. 48 miles per gallon

C. 55 miles per gallon

D. 35 miles per gallon

18) nine out of 45 students had to go to summer school. What is the ratio of students who did not have to go to summer school expressed, in its lowest terms?

Write your answer in the box below.

[   ]

19) A steak dinner at a restaurant costs $6.25. If a man buys a steak dinner for himself and 5 friends, what will the total cost be?

A. $31.125

B. $37.125

C. $35.50

D. $37.50

20) If 6 garbage trucks can collect the trash of 42 homes in a day. How many trucks are needed to collect in 140 houses?

A. 18

B. 12

C. 10

D. 20

STOP
This is the end of Unit 2

Unit 3

Calculators are NOT permitted for unit 3 of the test.

Read each question. Then mark your answers in your answer sheet.

If you have time, review your answers and only answer questions you did not answer in the unit.

Time for Unit 3: 60 Minutes

21) In a classroom of 56 students, 25 are male. About what percentage of the class is female?

   A. 53%

   B. 54%

   C. 55%

   D. 56%

22) A florist has 765 flowers. How many full bouquets of 15 flowers can he make?

   A. 45

   B. 49

   C. 53

   D. 51

23) What is 8,456.37651 rounded to the nearest tenth?

   A. 8,456.377

   B. 8,456.4

   C. 8,456

   D. 8,456.38

24) If a rectangular swimming pool has a perimeter of 156 feet and it is 33 feet wide, what is its area?

   A. 1,896 square feet

   B. 2,600 square feet

   C. 1,325 square feet

   D. 1,485 square feet

25) What is the volume of the following rectangle prism?

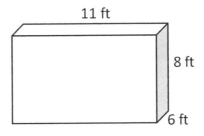

Write your answer in the box below.

26) A barista averages making 11 cups of coffee per hour. At this rate, how many hours will it take until she's made 880 cups of coffee?

A. 75

B. 80

C. 85

D. 90

27) Ava needs $\frac{1}{7}$ of an ounce of salt to make 1 cup of dip for fries. How many cups of dip will she be able to make if she has 80 ounces of salt?

A. 460

B. 56

C. 760

D. 560

28) A circle has a diameter of 6 inches. What is its approximate circumference? (π = 3.14)

    A. 4.71 inches

    B. 18.84 inches

    C. 37.68 inches

    D. 36.12 inches

29) How long is the line segment shown on the number line below?

Write your answer in the box below.

30) If $x = -1$, which equation is true?

    A. $x(4x - 8) = 20$

    B. $6(8 - 2x) = 60$

    C. $3(2x + 9) = 14$

    D. $4x - 5 = -12$

"This is the end of Practice Test 6"

Answer Keys

PARCC Practice Tests

❋ Now, it's time to review your results to see where you went wrong and what areas you need to improve!

Practice Test - 1

1	C	11	B	21	A
2	A	12	B	22	C
3	A	13	C	23	D
4	B	14	A	24	19
5	D	15	A	25	D
6	B	16	$\frac{1}{4}$	26	A
7	D	17	C	27	D
8	D	18	D	28	D
9	A	19	C	29	13
10	378	20	D	30	C

Practice Test - 2

1	C	11	A	21	C
2	D	12	B	22	D
3	B	13	D	23	B
4	D	14	C	24	D
5	D	15	B	25	336
6	B	16	C	26	B
7	C	17	C	27	D
8	C	18	$\frac{8}{9}$	28	B
9	A	19	D	29	10
10	B	20	D	30	B

Practice Test - 3

1	C	11	B	21	A
2	A	12	B	22	C
3	A	13	C	23	D
4	B	14	A	24	22
5	D	15	A	25	C
6	B	16	$\frac{1}{9}$	26	A
7	D	17	C	27	D
8	D	18	D	28	D
9	A	19	C	29	21
10	132	20	D	30	C

Practice Test - 4

1	C	11	A	21	C
2	D	12	B	22	D
3	B	13	D	23	B
4	D	14	C	24	D
5	D	15	B	25	210
6	B	16	C	26	B
7	C	17	C	27	D
8	C	18	$\frac{6}{7}$	28	B
9	A	19	B	29	10
10	B	20	D	30	B

Practice Test - 5

1	C	11	B	21	A
2	A	12	B	22	C
3	A	13	C	23	D
4	B	14	A	24	14
5	D	15	A	25	D
6	B	16	$\frac{1}{12}$	26	A
7	D	17	C	27	D
8	D	18	D	28	D
9	A	19	C	29	11
10	528	20	D	30	C

Practice Test - 6

1	C	11	A	21	C
2	D	12	B	22	D
3	B	13	D	23	B
4	D	14	C	24	D
5	D	15	B	25	528
6	B	16	C	26	B
7	C	17	C	27	D
8	C	18	$\frac{4}{5}$	28	B
9	A	19	D	29	10
10	B	20	D	30	B

Answers and Explanations

Practice Test 1

PARCC - Mathematics

Answers and Explanations

1) Answer: C.

To find the answer, subtract 21,890 from 22,010.

$22,010 - 21,890 = 120 \; miles$

2) Answer: A.

Let x be the new price after discount.

$x = 40 \times (100 - 15)\% = 40 \times 85\% = 40 \times 0.85 = 34 \Rightarrow x = \$34$

3) Answer: A.

Use area of rectangle formula.

area of a rectangle $= width \times length \Rightarrow D = w \times l \Rightarrow w = \dfrac{D}{l} = \dfrac{D}{19}$

4) Answer: B.

8 eggs for 1 cake. Therefore, 720 eggs can be used for $(720 \div 8)$ 90 cakes.

5) Answer: D.

To list the fractions from least to greatest, you can convert the fractions to decimal.

$\dfrac{3}{5} = 0.6; \dfrac{8}{9} = 0.889; \dfrac{7}{10} = 0.7; \dfrac{1}{2} = 0.5; \dfrac{2}{16} = 0.125$

$\dfrac{2}{16} = 0.125, \dfrac{1}{2} = 0.5, \dfrac{3}{5} = 0.6, \dfrac{7}{10} = 0.7, \dfrac{8}{9} = 0.889$

Option D shows the fractions in order from least to greatest.

6) Answer: B.

3 multiplied by $\dfrac{5}{4} = \dfrac{15}{4} = 3.75$, therefore, only choice B is correct.

7) Answer: D.

To find the selling price, multiply the price by (100% – rate of discount).

Then: $(160) (100\% - 24\%) = (160) (0.76) = 121.6$

8) Answer: D.

An acute angle is any angle larger than 0 and smaller than 90 degrees. From the options provided, only D (80 degrees) is smaller than 90.

9) Answer: A.

Plug in 30 for A in the equations. Only option A works.

$A + 40 = 70$

$30 + 40 = 70$

10) Answer: 378.

First, find the missing side of the trapezoid. The perimeter of the trapezoid below is 85. Therefore, the missing side of the trapezoid (its height) is:

$85 - 16 - 20 - 28 = 85 - 64 = 21$

Area of a trapezoid: $A = \frac{1}{2} h (b1 + b2)$

$= \frac{1}{2} (21) (16 + 20) = 378$

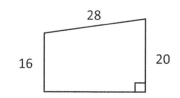

11) Answer: B.

Use area and circumference of circle formula.

Area of a circle $= \pi r^2 \Rightarrow 9\pi = \pi r^2 \Rightarrow r = 3$

Circumference of a circle $= 2\pi r \Rightarrow C = 2 \times 3 \times \pi \Rightarrow C = 6\pi$

12) Answer: B.

Alice drives 38 miles in one hour. Therefore, she drives 1,406 miles in about (1,406 ÷ 38) 37 hours.

13) Answer: C.

5 yards = 5 × 36 = 180 inches

9 feet = 9 × 12 = 108inches

5 yards 9 feet and 13 inches = 180 inches + 108 inches + 13 inches = 301 inches

14) Answer: A.

Simplify each option provided using order of operations rules.

A. $7 - (-5) + (-25) = 7 + 5 - 25 = -13$

B. $3 + (-3) \times (-9) = 3 + 27 = 30$

C. $-6 \times (-6) + (-4) \times (-9) = 36 + 36 = 72$

D. $(-7) \times (-4) + 5 = 28 + 5 = 33$

Only option A is -13.

15) Answer: A.

$$\frac{7}{8} \times \frac{4}{7} = \frac{7 \times 4}{8 \times 7} = \frac{28}{56} = \frac{1}{2}$$

16) Answer: $\frac{1}{4}$.

Use area of rectangle formula.

Area $= length \times width \Rightarrow A = \frac{7}{10} \times \frac{5}{14} \Rightarrow A = \frac{1}{4}$ inches

17) Answer: C.

ABC Corporation's income $= \frac{7}{3}$ management's predicted income.

$\$420,000 = \frac{7}{3}$ management's predicted income

management's predicted income $= \$420,000 \times \frac{3}{7} = \$180,000$

18) Answer: D.

Find the area of the room which is a square. Use area of square formula.

$S = a^2 \Rightarrow S = 11 \, feet \times 11 \, feet = 121$ square feet

19) Answer: C.

$$\frac{5}{7} + \frac{1}{2} - \frac{3}{14} = \frac{(5 \times 2) + (1 \times 7) - (1 \times 3)}{14} = \frac{14}{14} = 1$$

20) Answer: D.

Use percent formula:

$$part = \frac{percent}{100} \times whole$$

$896 = \frac{percent}{100} \times 2,800 \Rightarrow 896 = percent \times 28 \Rightarrow percent = 32$

21) Answer: A.

There are 84 cards in the bag and 12 of them are white. Then, 12 out of 84 cards are white. You can write this as: $\frac{12}{84}$. To simplify this fraction, divide both numerator and denominator by 12. Then: $\frac{12}{84} = \frac{1}{7}$

22) Answer: C.

1 meter of the rope = 280 grams

10.5 meter of the rope = 10.5 × 280 = 2,940 grams = 2.94 kilograms

23) Answer: D.

Lily eats 4 pancakes in 1 minute ⇒ Lily eats 4 × 8 pancakes in 8 minutes (32).

Ella eats $3\frac{1}{4}$ pancakes in 1 minute ⇒ Ella eats $3\frac{1}{4}×$ 8 pancakes in 8 minutes ($\frac{104}{4}$ =26).

In total Lily and Ella eat 32 + 26 = 58 pancakes in 8 minutes.

24) Answer: 19.

To solve this problem, divide $2\frac{5}{7}$ by $\frac{1}{7}$.

$2\frac{5}{7} ÷ \frac{1}{7} = \frac{19}{7} ÷ \frac{1}{7} = \frac{19}{7} × \frac{7}{1} = 19$

25) Answer: D.

The question is that number 486,124.8 is how many times of number 4.861248. The answer is 100,000.

26) Answer: A.

Use area of rectangle formula.

$A = a × b ⇒ A = 90 × 35 ⇒ A = 3,150$

Divide the area by 9 (3 × 3 = 9 squares) to find the number of squares needed.

$3,150 ÷ 9 = 350$

27) Answer: D.

Use volume of cube formula.

Volume= $length × width × height ⇒ V = 7 × 5 × 11 ⇒ V = 385 \ cm^3$

28) Answer: D.

Write the numbers in order: 10, 15, 21, 23, 27, 29, 31

Median is the number in the middle. Therefore, the median is 23.

29) Answer: 13.

Use PEMDAS (order of operation):

$7 + [10 × 9] ÷ 15 = 7 + (90) ÷ 15 = 7 + (90 ÷ 15) = 7 + 6 = 13$

30) Answer: C.

Use percent formula: part $= \frac{\text{percent}}{100} \times$ whole

$15 = \frac{\text{percent}}{100} \times 50 \Rightarrow 15 = \frac{\text{percent} \times 50}{100} \Rightarrow 15 = \frac{\text{percent} \times 5}{10}$, multiply both sides by 10.

$150 = \text{percent} \times 5$, divide both sides by 5. $\Rightarrow 30$ percent

Practice Test 2

PARCC - Mathematics

Answers and Explanations

1) Answer: C.

$32 + (14 \times 15) = 32 + 210 = 242$

2) Answer: D.

1 hour: $6.25; 5 hours: $5 \times \$6.25 = \$31.25$

3) Answer: B.

$5 - 3\frac{2}{5} = \frac{25}{5} - \frac{17}{5} = \frac{8}{5} = 1\frac{3}{5}$

4) Answer: D.

The number of guests that are not present are: $(240 - 180)$ 60 out of $240 = \frac{60}{240}$

Change the fraction to percent: $\frac{60}{240} \times 100\% = 25\%$

5) Answer: D.

Each kilogram is 1,000 grams.

$52,756$ grams $= \frac{52,756}{1,000} = 52.756$ kilograms. Therefore, two amounts provided are equal.

6) Answer: B.

Aria teaches 24 hours for four identical courses. Therefore, she teaches 6 hours for each course. Aria earns $30 per hour. Therefore, she earned $180 (6×30) for each course.

7) Answer: C.

The number of female students in the class is: $(80 - 48)$ 32 out of $80 = \frac{32}{80}$

Change the fraction to percent: $\frac{32}{80} \times 100\% = 40\%$

8) Answer: C.

Write a proportion and solve.

$\frac{6 \text{ soft drinks}}{18 \text{ guests}} = \frac{x}{210 \text{ guests}} \Rightarrow x = \frac{210 \times 6}{18} \Rightarrow x = 70$

9) Answer: A.

average (mean) = $\frac{\text{sum of terms}}{\text{number of terms}}$ ⇒ average = $\frac{5+7+15+15+23+26+33+36}{8}$ ⇒ average = 20

10) Answer: B.

Every 50 minutes Emma checks her email.

In 15 hours (900 minutes), Emma checks her email (900 ÷ 50) 18 times.

11) Answer: A.

Peter's speed = $\frac{160}{8}$ = 20

Jason's speed = $\frac{400}{8}$ = 50

$\frac{The\ average\ speed\ of\ peter}{The\ average\ speed\ of\ Jason} = \frac{20}{50}$ equals to: $\frac{2}{5}$ or 2: 5

12) Answer: B.

5 workers can walk 10 dogs ⇒ 1 workers can walk 2 dogs.

9 workers can walk (9 × 2) 18 dogs.

13) Answer: D.

In fractions, when denominators increase, the value of fractions decrease and as much as numerators increase, the value of fractions increase. Therefore, the least one of this list is: $\frac{1}{16}$ and the greatest one of this list is: $\frac{1}{3}$

14) Answer: C.

The horizontal axis in the coordinate plane is called the $x - axis$. The vertical axis is called the $y - axis$. The point at which the two axes intersect is called the origin. The origin is at 0 on the $x - axis$ and 0 on the $y - axis$.

15) Answer: B.

All angles in every triangle add up to 180°. Let x be the angle ABC.

Then: $180 = 72 + 48 + x \Rightarrow x = 60°$

16) Answer: C.

$3.95 per mile for the first 25 miles. Therefore, the cost for the first 25 miles is:

25 × $3.95 = $98.75

$4.15 per mile for each mile over 25, therefore, 4 miles over 25 miles cost:

$4 \times \$4.15 = \$16.6$

In total, David pays: $\$98.75 + \$16.6 = \$115.35$

17) Answer: C.

Write a proportion and solve. 25 gallons: 100 miles $\Rightarrow$ 1 gallon: $1,000 \div 25 = 40$ miles

18) Answer: $\frac{8}{9}$.

The students that had to go to summer school is 6 out of $54 = \frac{6}{54} = \frac{1}{9}$

Therefore $\frac{8}{9}$ students did not have to go to summer school.

19) Answer: D.

4 steak dinners = $4 \times \$4.75 = \$19$

20) Answer: D.

8 garbage trucks can collect the trash of 64 homes. Then, one garbage truck can collect the trash of 8 homes.

To collect trash of 160 houses, 20 $(160 \div 8)$ garbage trucks are required.

21) Answer: C.

There are 40 students in the class. 18 of the are male and 22 of them are female. 22 out of 40 are female. Then: $\frac{22}{40} = \frac{x}{100} \rightarrow 2,200 = 40x \rightarrow x = 2,200 \div 40 = 55\%$

22) Answer: D.

Divide the number flowers by 17: $833 \div 17 = 49$

23) Answer: B.

Rounding decimals is similar to rounding other numbers. If the hundredths and thousandths places of a decimal is fifty-nine or less, they are dropped, and the tenths place does not change. For example, rounding 0.921 to the nearest tenth would give 0.9. Therefore, 5,157.59325 rounded to the nearest tenth is 5,157.6.

24) Answer: D.

Perimeter of rectangle formula:

$P = 2 \, (length + width) \Rightarrow 110 = 2 \, (l + 21) \Rightarrow l = 34$

Area of rectangle formula: $A = length \times width \Rightarrow A = 34 \times 21 \Rightarrow A = 714$

25) Answer: 336.

Use volume of rectangle prism formula.

$V = length \times width \times height \Rightarrow V = 12 \times 7 \times 4 \Rightarrow V = 336$

26) Answer: B.

8 cups: 1 hour

600 cups: $600 \div 8 = 75$ hours

27) Answer: D.

Write a proportion and solve. $\frac{\frac{1}{5}}{56} = \frac{1}{x} \Rightarrow x = 56 \times 5 = 280$

28) Answer: B.

The diameter of the circle is 12 inches. Therefore, the radius of the circle is 6 inches.

Use circumference of circle formula.

$C = 2\pi r \Rightarrow C = 2 \times 3.14 \times 6 \Rightarrow C = 37.68$

29) Answer: 10.

The line segment is from 4 to -6. Therefore, the line is 10 units.

$4 - (-6) = 4 + 6 = 10$

30) Answer: B.

Plug in $x = -3$ in each equation.

A. $x(2x - 2) = 18 \rightarrow (-3)(2(-3) - 2) = (-3) \times (-6 - 2) = 24$

B. $3(6 - 3x) = 45 \rightarrow 3(6 - 3(-3)) = 3(6 + 9) = 3(15) = 45$

C. $4(3x + 7) = 16 \rightarrow 4(3(-3) + 7) = 4(-9 + 7) = 4(-2) = -8$

D. $6x - 8 = -15 \rightarrow 6(-3) - 8 = -18 - 8 = -26$

Only option B.

Practice Test 3

PARCC - Mathematics

Answers and Explanations

1) Answer: C.

To find the answer, subtract 43,907 from 44,053.

$44,053 - 43,907 = 146 \ miles$

2) Answer: A.

Let x be the new price after discount.

$x = 30 \times (100 - 40)\% = 50 \times 60\% = 30 \times 0.60 = 18 \Rightarrow x = \$18$

3) Answer: A.

Use area of rectangle formula.

$area \ of \ a \ rectangle = width \times length \Rightarrow D = w \times l \Rightarrow w = \frac{D}{l} = \frac{D}{7}$

4) Answer: B.

3 eggs for 1 cake. Therefore, 210 eggs can be used for $(210 \div 3)$ 70 cakes.

5) Answer: D.

To list the fractions from least to greatest, you can convert the fractions to decimal.

$\frac{3}{4} = 0.75; \frac{6}{7} = 0.86; \frac{2}{10} = 0.2; \frac{1}{2} = 0.5; \frac{6}{14} = 0.43$

$\frac{2}{10} = 0.2, \frac{6}{14} = 0.43, \frac{1}{2} = 0.5, \frac{3}{4} = 0.75, \frac{6}{7} = 0.86$

Option D shows the fractions in order from least to greatest.

6) Answer: B.

5 multiplied by $\frac{4}{3} = \frac{20}{3} = 6.66$, therefore, only choice B is correct.

7) Answer: D.

To find the selling price, multiply the price by (100% – rate of discount).

Then: $(150)(100\% - 10\%) = (150)(0.9) = 135$

8) Answer: D.

An obtuse angle is any angle larger than 90 degrees. From the options provided, only D (120 degrees) is larger than 90.

9) Answer: A.

Plug in 30 for A in the equations. Only option A works.

$A + 30 = 60$

$30 + 30 = 60$

10) Answer: 132.

First, find the missing side of the trapezoid. The perimeter of the trapezoid below is 50. Therefore, the missing side of the trapezoid (its height) is:

$50 - 10 - 16 - 12 = 50 - 38 = 12$

Area of a trapezoid: $A = \frac{1}{2} h \, (b1 + b2)$

$= \frac{1}{2} (12) (10 + 12) = 132$

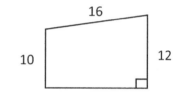

11) Answer: B.

Use area and circumference of circle formula.

Area of a circle $= \pi r^2 \Rightarrow 36\pi = \pi r^2 \Rightarrow r = 6$

Circumference of a circle $= 2\pi r \Rightarrow C = 2 \times 6 \times \pi \Rightarrow C = 12\pi$

12) Answer: B.

Alice drives 56 miles in one hour. Therefore, she drives 1960 miles in about $(1960 \div 56)$ 35 hours.

13) Answer: C.

10 yards = $10 \times 36 = 360$ inches

3 feet = $3 \times 12 = 36$ inches

10 yards 3 feet and 4 inches = 360 inches + 36 inches + 4 inches = 400 inches

14) Answer: A.

Simplify each option provided using order of operations rules.

A. $7 - (-3) + (-17) = 7 + 3 - 17 = -7$

B. $1 + (-3) \times (-2) = 1 + 6 = 7$

C.$-6 \times (-6) + (-2) \times (-12) = 36 + 24 = 60$

D.$(-2) \times (-7) + 4 = 14 + 4 = 18$

Only option A is -7.

15) Answer: A.

$$\frac{6}{8} \times \frac{4}{6} = \frac{6 \times 4}{8 \times 6} = \frac{24}{48} = \frac{1}{2}$$

16) Answer: $\frac{1}{9}$.

Use area of rectangle formula.

Area$= length \times width \Rightarrow A = \frac{5}{6} \times \frac{2}{15} \Rightarrow A = \frac{1}{9}$ inches

17) Answer: C.

ABC Corporation's income $= \frac{3}{2}$ management's predicted income.

$300,000 = \frac{3}{2}$ management's predicted income

management's predicted income $= \$300,000 \times \frac{2}{3} = \$200,000$

18) Answer: D.

Find the area of the room which is a square. Use area of square formula.

$S = a^2 \Rightarrow S = 16\,feet \times 16\,feet = 256$ square feet

19) Answer: C.

$$\frac{1}{2} + \frac{4}{7} - \frac{1}{14} = \frac{(7 \times 1) + (2 \times 4) - (1 \times 1)}{14} = \frac{14}{14} = 1$$

20) Answer: D.

Use percent formula:

$$\text{part} = \frac{\text{percent}}{100} \times \text{whole}$$

$900 = \frac{\text{percent}}{100} \times 3600 \Rightarrow 900 = \text{percent} \times 36 \Rightarrow \text{percent} = 25$

21) Answer: A.

There are 40 cards in the bag and 8 of them are white. Then, 8 out of 40 cards are white.

You can write this as: $\frac{8}{40}$. To simplify this fraction, divide both numerator and

denominator by 13. Then: $\frac{8}{40} = \frac{1}{5}$

22) Answer: C.

1 meter of the rope = 500 grams

12.2 meter of the rope = 12.2 × 500 = 6,100 grams = 6.1 kilograms

23) Answer: D.

Lily eats 3 pancakes in 1 minute ⇒ Lily eats 3 × 5 pancakes in 5 minutes (15).

Ella eats 2 ½ pancakes in 1 minute ⇒ Ella eats 2 ½ × 5 pancakes in 5 minutes

($\frac{25}{2}$ = 12.5).

In total Lily and Ella eat 15 + 12.5 = 27.5 pancakes in 5 minutes.

24) Answer: 22.

To solve this problem, divide $5\frac{1}{2}$ by $\frac{1}{4}$.

$$5\frac{1}{2} \div \frac{1}{4} = \frac{11}{2} \div \frac{1}{4} = \frac{11}{2} \times \frac{4}{1} = 22$$

25) Answer: C.

The question is that number 52,536.91 is how many times of number 5.253691. The answer is 10,000.

26) Answer: A.

Use area of rectangle formula.

$$A = a \times b \Rightarrow A = 52 \times 18 \Rightarrow A = 936$$

Divide the area by 9 (3 × 3 = 9 squares) to find the number of squares needed.

936 ÷ 9 = 104

27) Answer: D.

Use volume of cube formula.

$$Voluem = length \times width \times height \Rightarrow V = 7 \times 5 \times 9 \Rightarrow V = 315 \ cm^3$$

28) Answer: D.

Write the numbers in order: 9, 9, 10, 14, 15, 16, 18

Median is the number in the middle. Therefore, the median is 14.

29) Answer: 21.

Use PEMDAS (order of operation):

$$6 + [6 \times 5] \div 2 = 6 + (30) \div 2 = 6 + (30 \div 2) = 21$$

30) Answer: C.

Use percent formula: $\text{part} = \frac{\text{percent}}{100} \times \text{whole}$

$25 = \frac{\text{percent}}{100} \times 40 \Rightarrow 25 = \frac{\text{percent} \times 40}{100} \Rightarrow 25 = \frac{\text{percent} \times 4}{10}$, multiply both sides by 10.

$250 = \text{percent} \times 4$, divide both sides by 4. $\Rightarrow 62.5 = \text{percent}$

Practice Test 4

PARCC - Mathematics

Answers and Explanations

1) Answer: C.

$16 + (14 \times 22) = 16 + 308 = 324$

2) Answer: D.

1 hour: $4.75; 6 hours: $6 \times \$4.75 = \$28.5$

3) Answer: B.

$5 - 3\frac{2}{9} = \frac{45}{9} - \frac{29}{9} = \frac{16}{9} = 1\frac{7}{9}$

4) Answer: D.

The number of guests that are not present are: $(230 - 190)$ 40 out of $230 = \frac{40}{230}$

Change the fraction to percent: $\frac{40}{230} \times 100\% = 17.4\%$

5) Answer: D.

Each kilogram is 1,000 grams.

19,023 grams $= \frac{19,023}{1,000} = 19.023$ kilograms. Therefore, two amounts provided are equal.

6) Answer: B.

Aria teaches 24 hours for three identical courses. Therefore, she teaches 8 hours for each course. Aria earns $20 per hour. Therefore, she earned $160 (8×20) for each course.

7) Answer: C.

The number of female students in the class is: $(50 - 25)$ 25 out of $50 = \frac{25}{50}$

Change the fraction to percent: $\frac{25}{50} \times 100\% = 50\%$

8) Answer: C.

Write a proportion and solve.

$\frac{8 \text{ soft drinks}}{12 \text{ guests}} = \frac{x}{156 \text{ guests}} \Rightarrow x = \frac{156 \times 8}{12} \Rightarrow x = 104$

9) Answer: A.

average (mean) = $\frac{\text{sum of terms}}{\text{number of terms}}$ ⇒ average = $\frac{3+6+23+29+31+34+34+32}{8}$ ⇒ average = 24

10) Answer: B.

Every 90 minutes Emma checks her email.

In 12 hours (720 minutes), Emma checks her email (720 ÷ 90) 8 times.

11) Answer: A.

Peter's speed = $\frac{160}{4}$ = 40

Jason's speed = $\frac{240}{8}$ = 30

$\frac{\textit{The average speed of peter}}{\textit{The average speed of Jason}} = \frac{40}{30}$ equals to: $\frac{4}{3}$ or 4: 3

12) Answer: B.

3 workers can walk 9 dogs ⇒ 1 workers can walk 3 dogs.

6 workers can walk (6 × 3) 18 dogs.

13) Answer: D.

In fractions, when denominators increase, the value of fractions decrease and as much as numerators increase, the value of fractions increase. Therefore, the least one of this list is: $\frac{1}{10}$ and the greatest one of this list is: $\frac{1}{3}$

14) Answer: C.

The horizontal axis in the coordinate plane is called the $x - axis$. The vertical axis is called the $y - axis$. The point at which the two axes intersect is called the origin. The origin is at 0 on the $x - axis$ and 0 on the $y - axis$.

15) Answer: B.

All angles in every triangle add up to 180°. Let x be the angle ABC.

Then: $180 = 65 + 35 + x \Rightarrow x = 80°$

16) Answer: C.

$3.75 per mile for the first 20 miles. Therefore, the cost for the first 20 miles is:

20 × $3.75 = $75

$4.15 per mile for each mile over 20, therefore, 8 miles over 20 miles cost:

$8 \times \$4.15 = \$33.20$

In total, David pays: $\$75 + \$33.20 = \$108.20$

17) Answer: C.

Write a proportion and solve.

15 gallons: 675 miles $\Rightarrow$ 1 gallon: $675 \div 15 = 45$ miles

18) Answer: $\frac{6}{7}$.

The students that had to go to summer school is 5 out of $30 = \frac{5}{35} = \frac{1}{7}$

Therefore $\frac{6}{7}$ students did not have to go to summer school.

19) Answer: B.

4 steak dinners $= 4 \times \$8.5 = \$34$

20) Answer: D.

4 garbage trucks can collect the trash of 32 homes. Then, one garbage truck can collect the trash of 8 homes.

To collect trash of 80 houses, 10 $(80 \div 8)$ garbage trucks are required.

21) Answer: C.

There are 66 students in the class. 30 of the are male and 36 of them are female. 36 out of 66 are female. Then: $\frac{36}{66} = \frac{x}{100} \rightarrow 3,600 = 66x \rightarrow x = 3,600 \div 66 = 54.54.. \approx 55\%$

22) Answer: D.

Divide the number flowers by 13: $585 \div 13 = 45$

23) Answer: B.

Rounding decimals is similar to rounding other numbers. If the hundredths and thousandths places of a decimal is forty-nine or less, they are dropped, and the tenths place does not change. For example, rounding 0.843 to the nearest tenth would give 0.8. Therefore, 6,123.48245 rounded to the nearest tenth is 6,123.5.

24) Answer: D.

Perimeter of rectangle formula:

$P = 2 \, (length \, + \, width) \Rightarrow 124 = 2 \, (l + 24) \Rightarrow l = 38$

Area of rectangle formula: $A = length \times width \Rightarrow A = 38 \times 24 \Rightarrow A = 912$

25) Answer: 210.

Use volume of rectangle prism formula.

$V = length \times width \times height \Rightarrow V = 7 \times 5 \times 6 \Rightarrow V = 210$

26) Answer: B.

12 cups: 1 hour

1080 cups: $1080 \div 12 = 90$ hours

27) Answer: D.

Write a proportion and solve. $\dfrac{\frac{1}{5}}{60} = \dfrac{1}{x} \Rightarrow x = 60 \times 5 = 300$

28) Answer: B.

The diameter of the circle is 4 inches. Therefore, the radius of the circle is 2 inches. Use circumference of circle formula.

$C = 2\pi r \Rightarrow C = 2 \times 3.14 \times 2 \Rightarrow C = 12.56$

29) Answer: 10.

The line segment is from 3 to -7. Therefore, the line is 9 units.

$3 - (-7) = 3 + 7 = 10$

30) Answer: B.

Plug in $x = -2$ in each equation.

A. $x(2x - 4) = 50 \rightarrow (-2)(2(-2) - 4) = (-2) \times (-4 - 4) = 16$

B. $8(4 - x) = 48 \rightarrow 8(4 - (-2)) = 8(6) = 48$

C. $2(4x + 6) = 10 \rightarrow 2(4(-2) + 6) = 2(-8 + 6) = -4$

D. $6x - 2 = -23 \rightarrow 6(-2) - 2 = -12 - 2 = -14$

Only option B.

Practice Test 5

PARCC - Mathematics

Answers and Explanations

1) Answer: C.

To find the answer, subtract 54,815 from 55,015.

$55,015 - 54,815 = 200 \; miles$

2) Answer: A.

Let x be the new price after discount.

$x = 50 \times (100 - 20)\% = 50 \times 80\% = 50 \times 0.80 = 40 \Rightarrow x = \$40$

3) Answer: A.

Use area of rectangle formula.

area of a rectangle $= \; width \times length \Rightarrow D = w \times l \Rightarrow w = \dfrac{D}{l} = \dfrac{D}{10}$

4) Answer: B.

6 eggs for 1 cake. Therefore, 300 eggs can be used for $(300 \div 6)$ 50 cakes.

5) Answer: D.

To list the fractions from least to greatest, you can convert the fractions to decimal.

$\dfrac{2}{3} = 0.667; \dfrac{5}{8} = 0.625; \dfrac{3}{10} = 0.3; \dfrac{1}{4} = 0.25; \dfrac{5}{16} = 0.313$

$\dfrac{1}{4} = 0.25, \dfrac{3}{10} = 0.\,3, \dfrac{5}{16} = 0.313, \dfrac{5}{8} = 0.625, \dfrac{2}{3} = 0.667$

Option D shows the fractions in order from least to greatest.

6) Answer: B.

2 multiplied by $\dfrac{7}{3} = \dfrac{14}{3} = 4.66$, therefore, only choice B is correct.

7) Answer: D.

To find the selling price, multiply the price by (100% – rate of discount).

Then: (250) (100% – 30%) = (250) (0.7) = 175

8) Answer: D.

An acute angle is any angle larger than 0 and smaller than 90 degrees. From the options provided, only D (50 degrees) is smaller than 90.

9) Answer: A.

Plug in 40 for A in the equations. Only option A works.

$A + 50 = 90$

$40 + 50 = 90$

10) Answer: 528.

First, find the missing side of the trapezoid. The perimeter of the trapezoid below is 50. Therefore, the missing side of the trapezoid (its height) is:

$100 - 20 - 32 - 24 = 100 - 76 = 24$

Area of a trapezoid: A $= \frac{1}{2}$ h (b1 + b2)

$= \frac{1}{2} (24) (20 + 24) = 528$

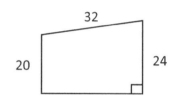

11) Answer: B.

Use area and circumference of circle formula.

Area of a circle $= \pi r^2 \Rightarrow 16\pi = \pi r^2 \Rightarrow r = 4$

Circumference of a circle $= 2\pi r \Rightarrow C = 2 \times 4 \times \pi \Rightarrow C = 8\pi$

12) Answer: B.

Alice drives 42 miles in one hour. Therefore, she drives 1,890 miles in about (1,890 ÷ 42) 45 hours.

13) Answer: C.

6 yards = 6 × 36 = 216 inches

8 feet = 8 × 12 = 96 inches

6 yards 8 feet and 10 inches = 216 inches + 96 inches + 10 inches = 322 inches

14) Answer: A.

Simplify each option provided using order of operations rules.

A. $8 - (-4) + (-22) = 8 + 4 - 22 = -10$

B. $2 + (-4) \times (-5) = 2 + 20 = 22$

C.$-5 \times (-5) + (-3) \times (-13) = 25 + 39 = 64$

D.$(-5) \times (-6) + 8 = 30 + 8 = 38$

Only option A is -10.

15) Answer: A.

$$\frac{5}{9} \times \frac{3}{5} = \frac{5 \times 3}{9 \times 5} = \frac{15}{45} = \frac{1}{3}$$

16) Answer: $\frac{1}{12}$.

Use area of rectangle formula.

Area$= length \times width \Rightarrow A = \frac{4}{9} \times \frac{3}{16} \Rightarrow A = \frac{1}{12}$ inches

17) Answer: C.

ABC Corporation's income $= \frac{5}{3}$ management's predicted income.

$\$600,000 = \frac{5}{3}$ management's predicted income

management's predicted income $= \$600,000 \times \frac{3}{5} = \$360,000$

18) Answer: D.

Find the area of the room which is a square. Use area of square formula.

$S = a^2 \Rightarrow S = 13\ feet \times 13\ feet = 169$ square feet

19) Answer: C.

$$\frac{2}{3} + \frac{3}{5} - \frac{10}{15} = \frac{(5 \times 2) + (3 \times 3) - (1 \times 10)}{15} = \frac{9}{15} = \frac{3}{5}$$

20) Answer: D.

Use percent formula:

$$\text{part} = \frac{\text{percent}}{100} \times \text{whole}$$

$840 = \frac{\text{percent}}{100} \times 4,200 \Rightarrow 840 = \text{percent} \times 42 \Rightarrow \text{percent} = 20$

21) Answer: A.

There are 50 cards in the bag and 10 of them are white. Then, 10 out of 50 cards are white. You can write this as: $\frac{10}{50}$. To simplify this fraction, divide both numerator and denominator by 10. Then: $\frac{10}{50} = \frac{1}{5}$

22) Answer: C.

1 meter of the rope = 650 grams

11.8 meter of the rope = $11.8 \times 650 = 7,670$ grams = 7.67 kilograms

23) Answer: D.

Lily eats 5 pancakes in 1 minute ⇒ Lily eats 5×6 pancakes in 6 minutes (30).

Ella eats $4\frac{1}{3}$ pancakes in 1 minute ⇒ Ella eats $4\frac{1}{3} \times 6$ pancakes in 6 minutes ($\frac{78}{3} = 26$).

In total Lily and Ella eat 30 + 26=56 pancakes in 6 minutes.

24) Answer: 14.

To solve this problem, divide $4\frac{2}{3}$ by $\frac{1}{3}$.

$$4\frac{2}{3} \div \frac{1}{3} = \frac{14}{3} \div \frac{1}{3} = \frac{14}{3} \times \frac{3}{1} = 14$$

25) Answer: D.

The question is that number 634,636.7 is how many times of number 6.346367. The answer is 100,000.

26) Answer: A.

Use area of rectangle formula.

$A = a \times b \Rightarrow A = 80 \times 24 \Rightarrow A = 1,920$

Divide the area by 16 ($4 \times 4 = 16$ squares) to find the number of squares needed.

$1,920 \div 16 = 120$

27) Answer: D.

Use volume of cube formula.

Volume= $length \times width \times height \Rightarrow V = 8 \times 6 \times 10 \Rightarrow V = 480\ cm^3$

28) Answer: D.

Write the numbers in order: 9, 19, 20, 24, 25, 26, 28

Median is the number in the middle. Therefore, the median is 24.

29) Answer: 11.

Use PEMDAS (order of operation):

$9 + [4 \times 8] \div 16 = 9 + (32) \div 16 = 9 + (32 \div 16) = 9+2=11$

30) Answer: C.

Use percent formula: $\text{part} = \frac{\text{percent}}{100} \times \text{whole}$

$35 = \frac{\text{percent}}{100} \times 80 \Rightarrow 35 = \frac{\text{percent} \times 80}{100} \Rightarrow 35 = \frac{\text{percent} \times 8}{10}$, multiply both sides by 10.

$350 = \text{percent} \times 8$, divide both sides by 8. $\Rightarrow 43.75 = \text{percent}$

Practice Test 6

PARCC - Mathematics

Answers and Explanations

1) Answer: C.

$26 + (24 \times 32) = 26 + 768 = 794$

2) Answer: D.

1 hour: $5.75; 7 hours: $7 \times \$5.75 = \$40.25$

3) Answer: B.

$6 - 4\frac{1}{7} = \frac{42}{7} - \frac{29}{7} = \frac{13}{7} = 1\frac{6}{7}$

4) Answer: D.

The number of guests that are not present are: (350 – 280) 70 out of $350 = \frac{70}{350}$

Change the fraction to percent: $\frac{70}{350} \times 100\% = 20\%$

5) Answer: D.

Each kilogram is 1,000 grams.

28,045 grams $= \frac{28,045}{1,000} = 28.045$ kilograms. Therefore, two amounts provided are equal.

6) Answer: B.

Aria teaches 21 hours for three identical courses. Therefore, she teaches 7 hours for each course. Aria earns $25 per hour. Therefore, she earned $175 ($7 \times 25$) for each course.

7) Answer: C.

The number of female students in the class is: (70 – 42) 28 out of $70 = \frac{28}{70}$

Change the fraction to percent: $\frac{28}{70} \times 100\% = 40\%$

8) Answer: C.

Write a proportion and solve.

$\frac{5 \text{ soft drinks}}{14 \text{ guests}} = \frac{x}{280 \text{ guests}} \Rightarrow x = \frac{280 \times 5}{14} \Rightarrow x = 100$

9) Answer: A.

$$\text{average (mean)} = \frac{\text{sum of terms}}{\text{number of terms}} \Rightarrow \text{average} = \frac{4+5+10+14+24+31+35+37}{8} \Rightarrow \text{average} = 20$$

10) Answer: B.

Every 80 minutes Emma checks her email.

In 16 hours (960 minutes), Emma checks her email (960 ÷ 80) 12 times.

11) Answer: A.

Peter's speed $= \frac{210}{7} = 30$

Jason's speed $= \frac{360}{9} = 40$

$\frac{The\ average\ speed\ of\ peter}{The\ average\ speed\ of\ Jason} = \frac{30}{40}$ equals to: $\frac{3}{4}$ or $3:4$

12) Answer: B.

2 workers can walk 8 dogs $\Rightarrow$ 1 workers can walk 4 dogs.

7 workers can walk (7 × 4) 28 dogs.

13) Answer: D.

In fractions, when denominators increase, the value of fractions decrease and as much as numerators increase, the value of fractions increase. Therefore, the least one of this list is: $\frac{1}{11}$ and the greatest one of this list is: $\frac{1}{4}$

14) Answer: C.

The horizontal axis in the coordinate plane is called the $x-axis$. The vertical axis is called the $y-axis$. The point at which the two axes intersect is called the origin. The origin is at 0 on the $x-axis$ and 0 on the $y-axis$.

15) Answer: B.

All angles in every triangle add up to $180°$. Let x be the angle ABC.

Then: $180 = 60 + 45 + x \Rightarrow x = 75°$

16) Answer: C.

$4.25 per mile for the first 30 miles. Therefore, the cost for the first 30 miles is:

30 × $4.25 = $127.5

$4.75 per mile for each mile over 30, therefore, 9 miles over 30 miles cost:

$9 \times \$4.75 = \$42.75$

In total, David pays: $\$127.5 + \$42.75 = \$170.25$

17) Answer: C.

Write a proportion and solve. 18 gallons: 990 miles $\Rightarrow$ 1 gallon: $990 \div 18 = 55$ miles

18) Answer: $\frac{4}{5}$.

The students that had to go to summer school is 9 out of $45 = \frac{9}{45} = \frac{1}{5}$

Therefore $\frac{4}{5}$ students did not have to go to summer school.

19) Answer: D.

6 steak dinners $= 6 \times \$6.25 = \$37.5$

20) Answer: D.

6 garbage trucks can collect the trash of 42 homes. Then, one garbage truck can collect the trash of 7 homes.

To collect trash of 140 houses, 20 $(140 \div 7)$ garbage trucks are required.

21) Answer: C.

There are 56 students in the class. 25 of the are male and 31 of them are female. 31 out of 56 are female. Then: $\frac{31}{56} = \frac{x}{100} \rightarrow 3{,}100 = 56x \rightarrow x = 3{,}100 \div 56 = 55.35.. \approx 55\%$

22) Answer: D.

Divide the number flowers by 15: $765 \div 15 = 51$

23) Answer: B.

Rounding decimals is similar to rounding other numbers. If the hundredths and thousandths places of a decimal is thirty-seven or less, they are dropped, and the tenths place does not change. For example, rounding 0.843 to the nearest tenth would give 0.8. Therefore, 8,456.37651 rounded to the nearest tenth is 8,456.4.

24) Answer: D.

Perimeter of rectangle formula:

$P = 2\,(length \ + \ width) \Rightarrow 156 = 2\,(l + 33) \Rightarrow l = 45$

Area of rectangle formula: $A \ = \ length \ \times \ width \Rightarrow A = 45 \times 33 \Rightarrow A = 1{,}485$

25) Answer: 528.

Use volume of rectangle prism formula.

$V = length \times width \times height \Rightarrow V = 11 \times 6 \times 8 \Rightarrow V = 528$

26) Answer: B.

11 cups: 1 hour

880 cups: $880 \div 11 = 80$ hours

27) Answer: D.

Write a proportion and solve. $\dfrac{\frac{1}{7}}{80} = \dfrac{1}{x} \Rightarrow x = 80 \times 7 = 560$

28) Answer: B.

The diameter of the circle is 6 inches. Therefore, the radius of the circle is 3 inches. Use circumference of circle formula.

$C = 2\pi r \Rightarrow C = 2 \times 3.14 \times 3 \Rightarrow C = 18.84$

29) Answer: 10.

The line segment is from 9 to -1. Therefore, the line is 10 units.

$9 - (-1) = 9 + 1 = 10$

30) Answer: B.

Plug in $x = -1$ in each equation.

A. $x(4x - 8) = 20 \rightarrow (-1)(4(-1) - 8) = (-1) \times (-4 - 8) = 12$

B. $6(8 - 2x) = 60 \rightarrow 6(8 - 2(-1)) = 6(8 + 2) = 6(10) = 60$

C. $3(2x + 9) = 14 \rightarrow 3(2(-1) + 9) = 3(-2 + 9) = 3(7) = 21$

D. $4x - 5 = -12 \rightarrow 4(-1) - 5 = -4 - 5 = -9$

Only option B.

"End"

Made in the USA
Las Vegas, NV
25 April 2024